DRAW A MAP OF AN IMAGINARY COUNTRY

What is it called?

Mark its capital city, and include mountains, rivers, seas, forests, monuments and national dishes. Draw yourself as a king or queen.

COLOUR THE CONTINENTS

Use a different colour to fill every continent in the world: North America, South America, Africa, Europe, Asia, Antarctica and Australia/Oceania.

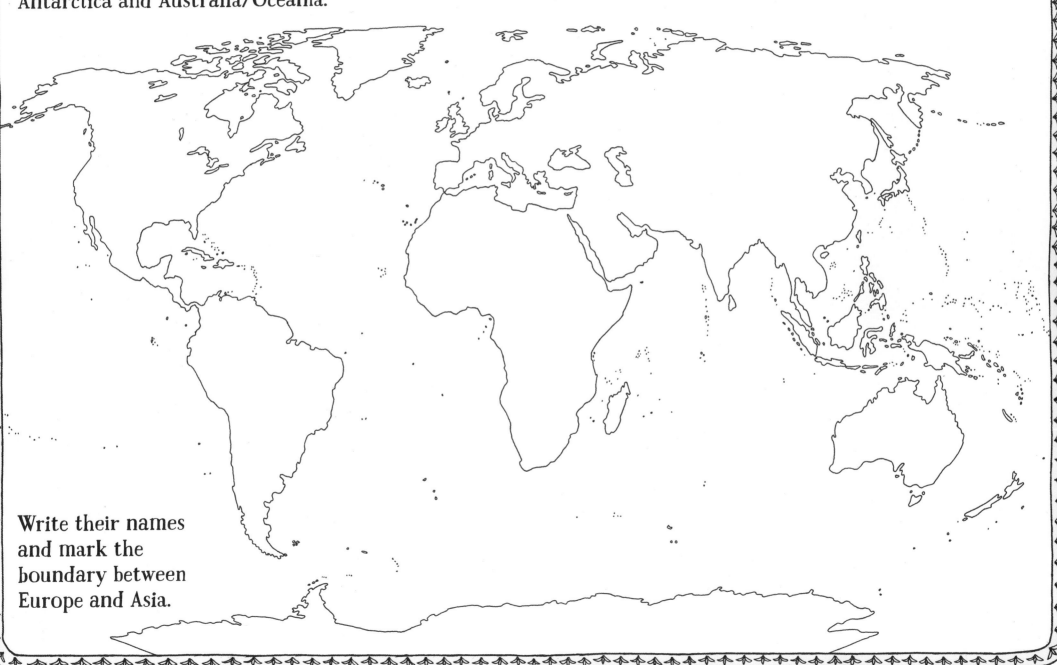

Write their names and mark the boundary between Europe and Asia.

Antarctica is the highest, driest, coldest and windiest continent. Few species live there year-round, but do you know some animals that visit?

Explore the Amazon

Imagine that you are an explorer in the Amazon rainforest in South America. Draw the animals, trees, people and plants that you see around you.

More than half of the Amazon rainforest is located in Brazil, but parts of it are located in other South American countries including Peru, Venezuela, Ecuador, Colombia, Guyana, Bolivia, Suriname and French Guiana. It is home to around 10% of all the animal species in the world as well as over 80,000 plant species.

DESERT LIFE

Death Valley, in the western United States, is one of the hottest and driest deserts in the world. Some of its landscape looks like this. Continue the pattern of the dry, cracked earth. Find out what animals and plants live there, then draw them here.

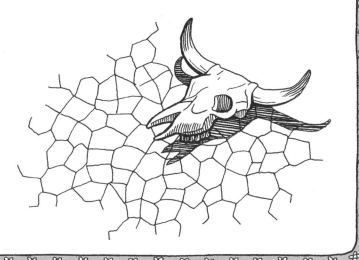

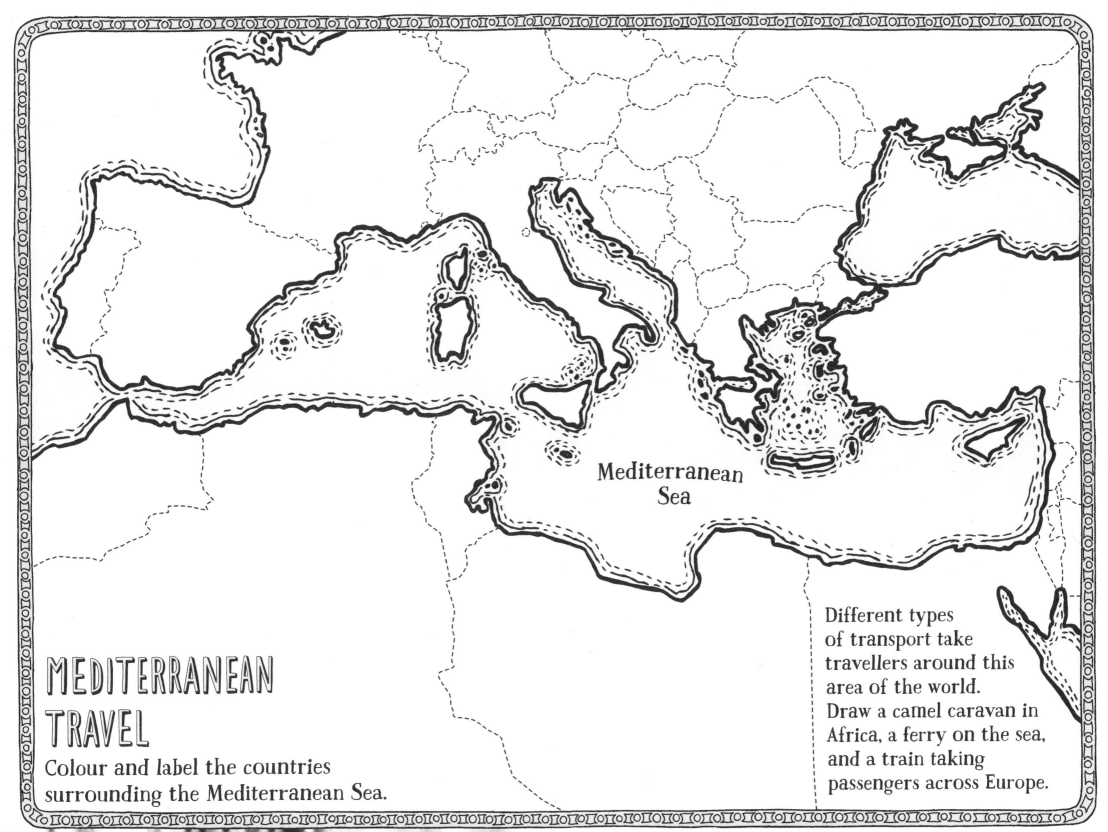

Mediterranean
Sea

MEDITERRANEAN
TRAVEL
Colour and label the countries
surrounding the Mediterranean Sea.

Different types
of transport take
travellers around this
area of the world.
Draw a camel caravan in
Africa, a ferry on the sea,
and a train taking
passengers across Europe.

The Suez Canal connects the Mediterranean Sea and the Red Sea. It is 120 miles long.

MAYAN LANGUAGE

The Mayan people invented the most advanced form of writing in the ancient Americas, with hundreds of different glyphs or symbols (pictures that are used to represent a language). Invent your own glyphs. What do your symbols mean?

In addition to having a complex written language, the Maya devised a numerical system, which they used for engineering, farming and astronomy. They also developed a very precise calendar system — one that is even more accurate than the one we use today!

Decorate this
INDIAN
ELEPHANT

In the state of Kerala on the southwest coast of India, many Hindu temples own elephants that have been domesticated, or are trained to live with humans. During festivals these elephants are richly decorated and participate in festivities, carrying statues representing Hindu gods on their backs.

Draw some animals that live in

AUSTRALIA

Australia is home to the world's largest living marsupial: the red kangaroo. It lives in the deserts and grasslands of Australia, and while the males are usually red, females can be grey, red or even a bluish grey!

SPORTS

are popular all over the world.
Draw sports that are played
in different countries around
the globe.

Mongolia

Japan

India

United Kingdom

South Africa

Namibia

Switzerland

USA

Brazil

New Zealand

Canada

Dance and music are important parts of culture.
Can you draw MUSICAL INSTRUMENTS or TYPES OF DANCE from these countries?

Russia

Spain

India

Brazil

Ghana

United Kingdom

Originating in the southern region of Andalucía in Spain, flamenco is a form of folk music and dance. It is made up of three parts: guitar playing, flamenco song and dance. The flamenco dancers perform intricate stamping patterns that create rhythmical beats to support the guitar.

Imagine that an alien fleet is invading Tokyo, Japan, and a team of **GIANT ROBOTS** is here to defend it. Draw what happens.

Kodomo no Hi, or Children's Day, is a national holiday in Japan that celebrates children. Traditional cakes made of rice called 'kashiwa-mochi' are served on this day.

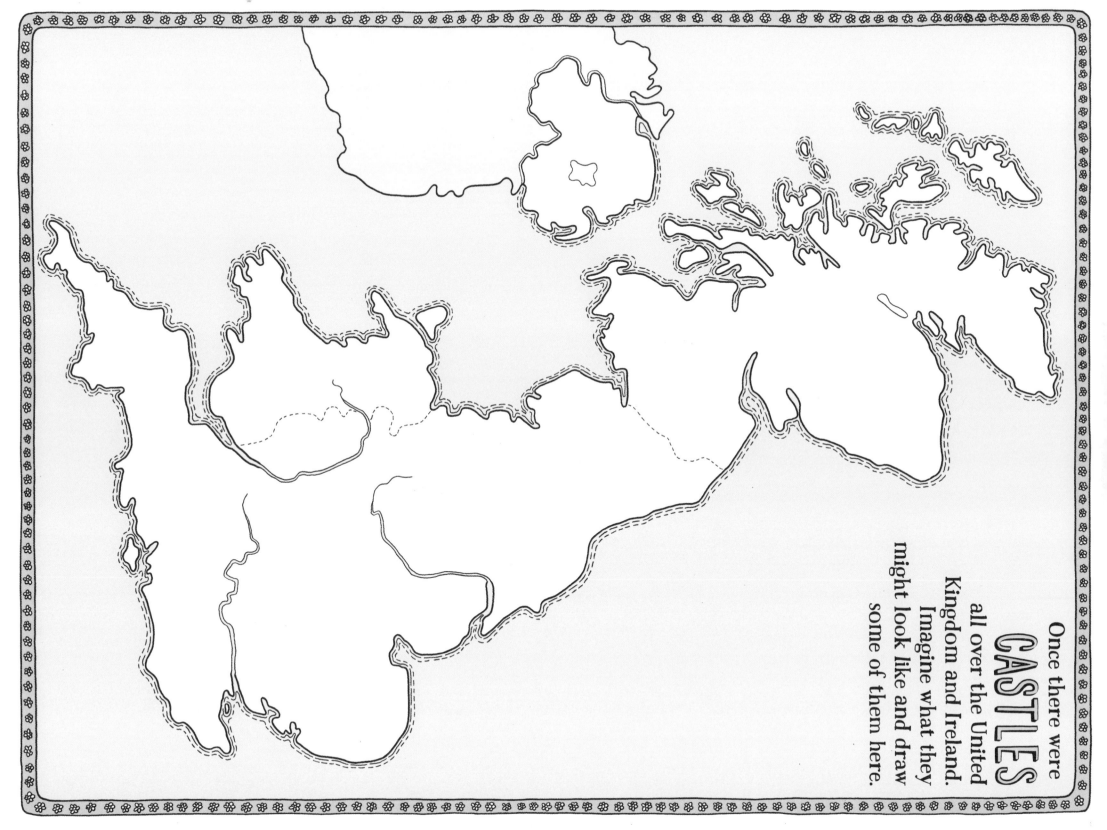

Once there were
CASTLES
all over the United
Kingdom and Ireland.
Imagine what they
might look like and draw
some of them here.

The largest and oldest continually occupied castle in the world is Windsor Castle in England, where Queen Elizabeth lives. It has been in use for almost one thousand years.

Three friends from Japan, Italy and Morocco are

SHARING A MEAL

and each of them has prepared a popular dish from their home country. Draw these dishes here.

Do you like soup? In China, one of the most exclusive traditional dishes is bird's nest soup. It is made out of the solidified saliva that swallows use to make their nests. Yum!

COLOUR THE FLAGS around the edge of this page and DESIGN YOUR OWN below.

Poland

Vietnam

France

Germany

Switzerland

United Kingdom

Bahrain

Czech Republic

Brazil

Netherlands

Sweden

Seychelles

Turkey

Canada

Greece

Macedonia

Republic of the Congo

Spain

The only national flag that is not rectangular or square is the flag of Nepal. It has a double triangle shape. It is red with a blue border and includes white symbols representing the sun and moon.

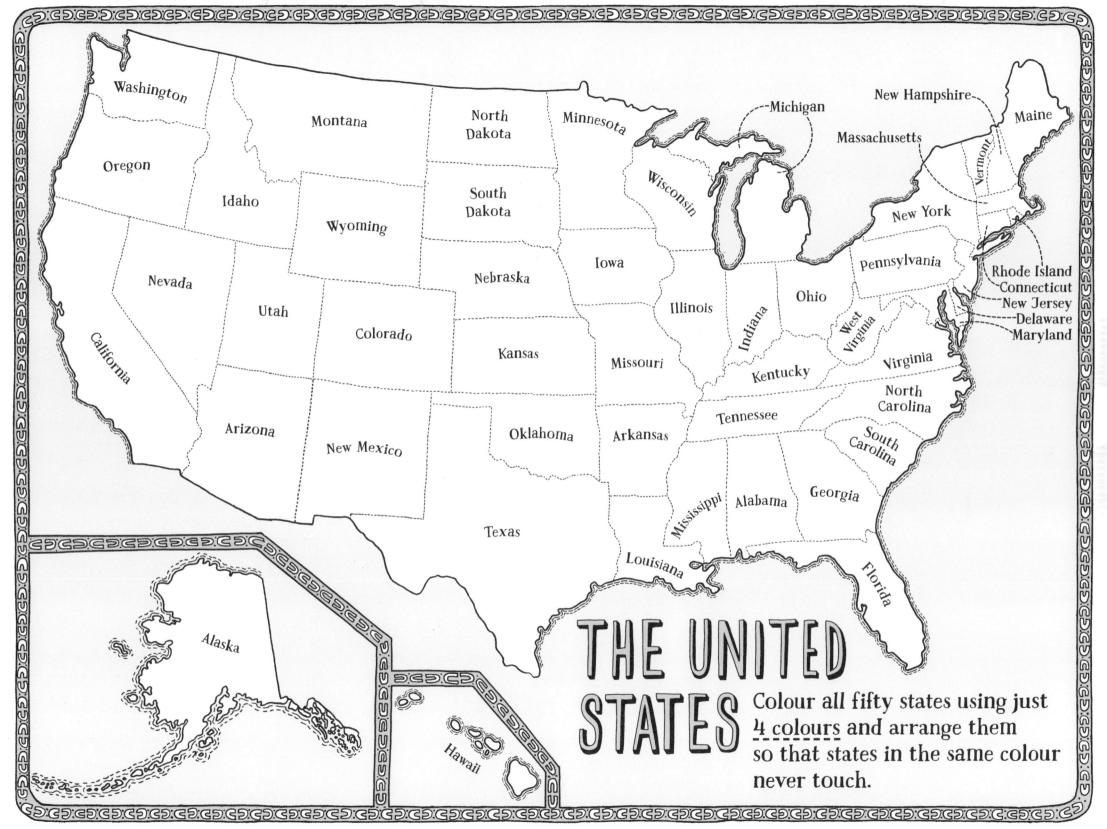

THE UNITED STATES

Colour all fifty states using just 4 colours and arrange them so that states in the same colour never touch.

White storks migrate from Europe to Africa for the winter. In search of air currents to coast on (which aren't usually found over the Mediterranean), they detour either over the Middle East or the Strait of Gibraltar.

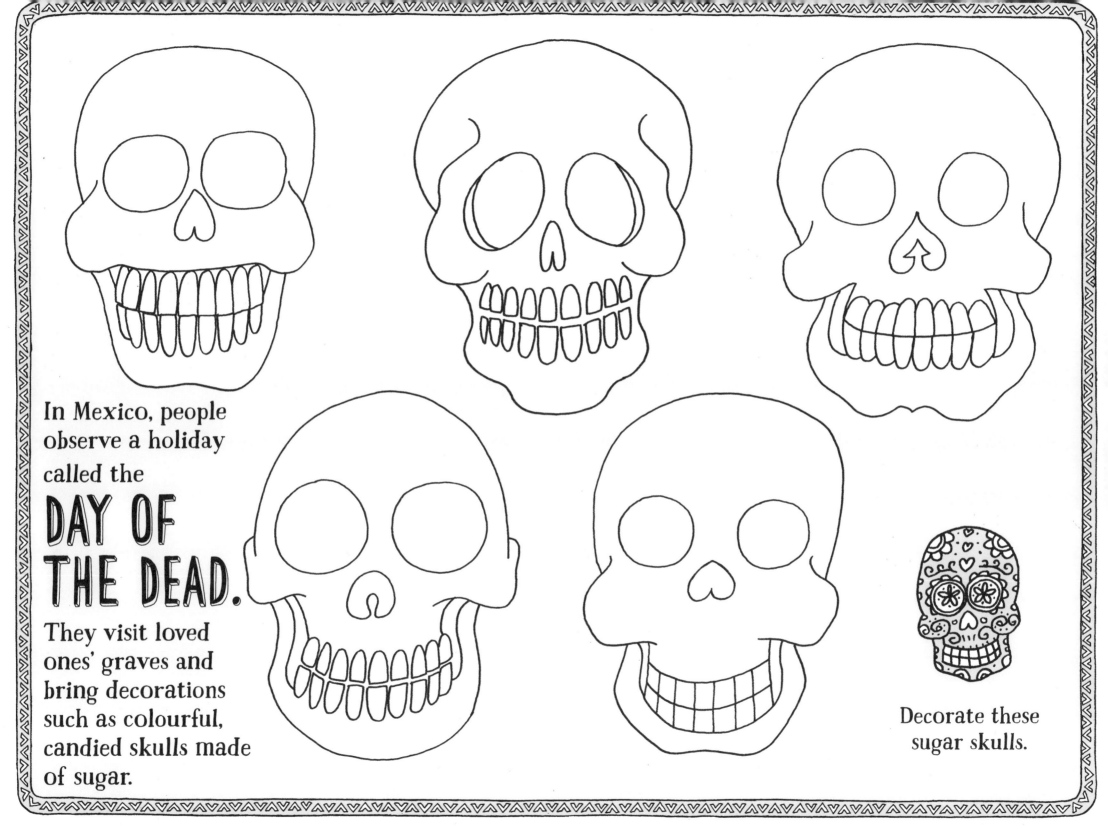

In Mexico, people observe a holiday called the

DAY OF THE DEAD.

They visit loved ones' graves and bring decorations such as colourful, candied skulls made of sugar.

Decorate these sugar skulls.

The Day of the Dead is celebrated on November 2nd. Its purpose is to honour family members who have died. Similar holidays have been celebrated by indigenous groups in Mexico as far back as three thousand years ago.

Draw these famous
LANDMARKS
alongside this map of
EUROPE
labelling each with the number of the city where it can be found.

THE EIFFEL TOWER

BRAN CASTLE

THE LEANING TOWER OF PISA

LA SAGRADA FAMÍLIA

THE BRANDENBURG GATE

BIG BEN

EDINBURGH CASTLE

THE PARTHENON

THE COLOSSEUM

EDINBURGH

United Kingdom

LONDON ①

BERLIN ④

Germany

PARIS ②

France

Italy

PISA ⑦

BARCELONA ③

Spain

ROME ⑧

Romania

BRAN ⑨

Greece
ATHENS ⑤

ART DOWN UNDER
The indigenous people of Australia are famous for their dot paintings. Finish the painting below, using the traditional colours of yellow, red, brown and white.

The original inhabitants of Australia and its nearby islands are known as Aboriginal people. Their art is based on important ancient stories and symbols centred on the Dreamtime, the time they believe the world was created. The Dreamtime stories are more than 50,000 years old, and have been handed down from one generation to the next.

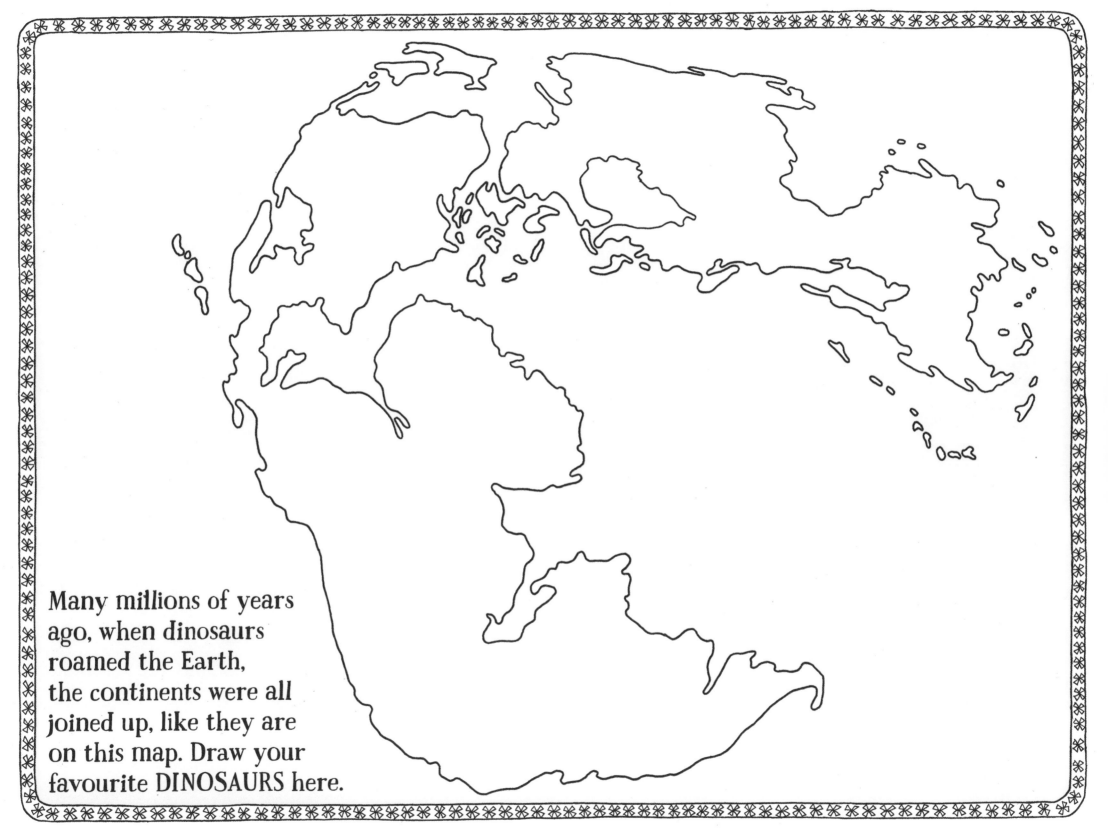

Many millions of years ago, when dinosaurs roamed the Earth, the continents were all joined up, like they are on this map. Draw your favourite DINOSAURS here.

Towards the end of the Jurassic period, about 150 million years ago, the first birds evolved from small flying dinosaurs.

Draw the Italian volcano
MOUNT VESUVIUS
as it erupts.

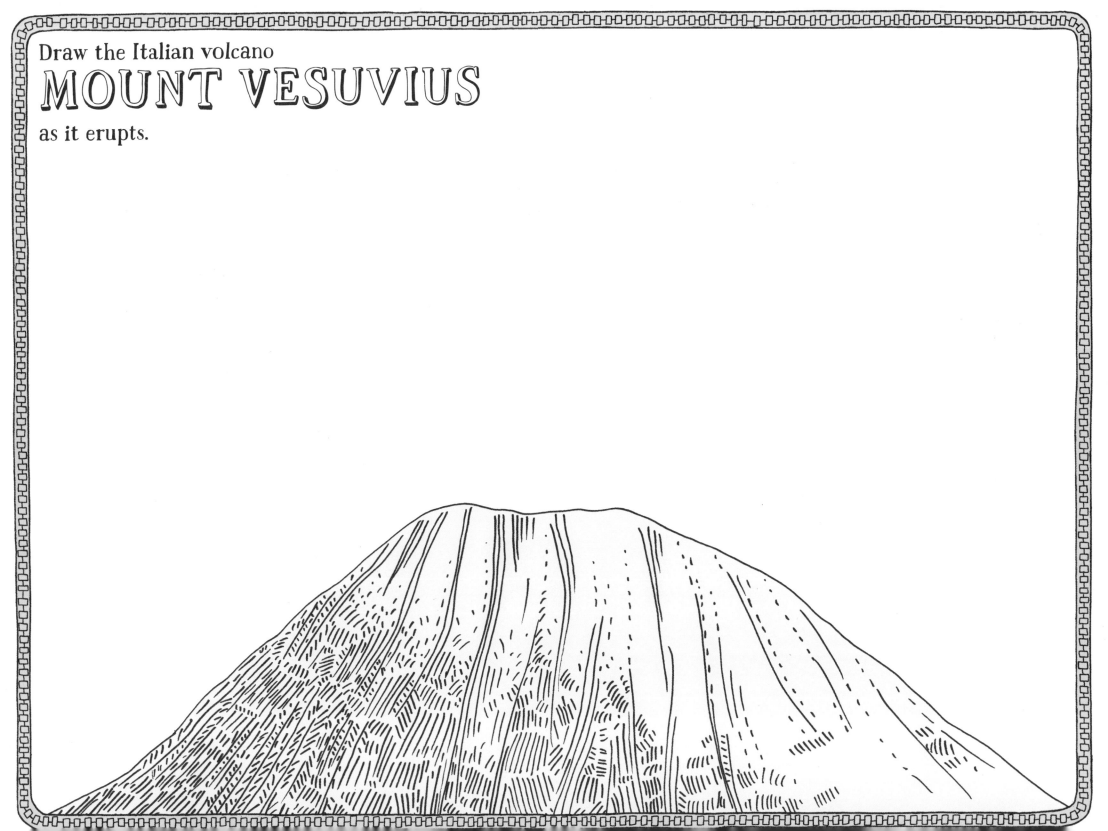

The biggest active volcano in Europe is Mount Etna in Sicily, Italy. It is 3329 metres high, and is one of the most active volcanoes in the world today.

start

A Greek
myth tells
the story
of a minotaur –
a man with a
bull's head –
imprisoned
in a great labyrinth.
Find your way to the cave of

THE MINOTAUR.

Do you know the difference between a maze and a labyrinth? A labyrinth has only one path to and from its centre, while a maze has many possible paths.

Imagine that you have discovered a

DESERT ISLAND

Draw what you find there.

The biggest uninhabited island on Earth is Devon Island, located in Baffin Bay, Canada. It is a very cold, dry, empty place — a bit like the planet Mars. In fact, some scientists sending experiments to Mars first try them out on Devon Island. It is the perfect training ground, but not a great holiday destination!

In Thailand, goods are sometimes sold directly out of boats. Draw what a FLOATING MARKET might look like when seen from above.

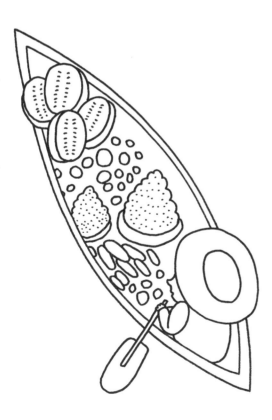

One of the smelliest fruits in the world is called a durian, which can be found in Southeast Asia. It smells a bit like a mixture of rotten meat, rotten onions and sweaty socks! Its flavour, however, is a different story. It is considered to be one of the world's most delicious fruits. Just remember to hold your nose when eating one!

HOW BIG IS BIG?

☐ = 100,000 square kilometres

Compare the sizes of countries by colouring the squares below according to their approximate sizes listed here.

(So Canada will need 100 squares!)

Canada: 10,000,000 km²
Egypt: 1,000,000 km²
Iceland: 100,000 km²
India: 3,300,000 km²
Italy: 300,000 km²
Mongolia: 1,600,000 km²

Namibia: 800,000 km²
Poland: 300,000 km²
Russia: 17,100,000 km²
Spain: 500,000 km²
Thailand: 500,000 km²
USA: 9,800,000 km²

Each square represents 100,000 km²

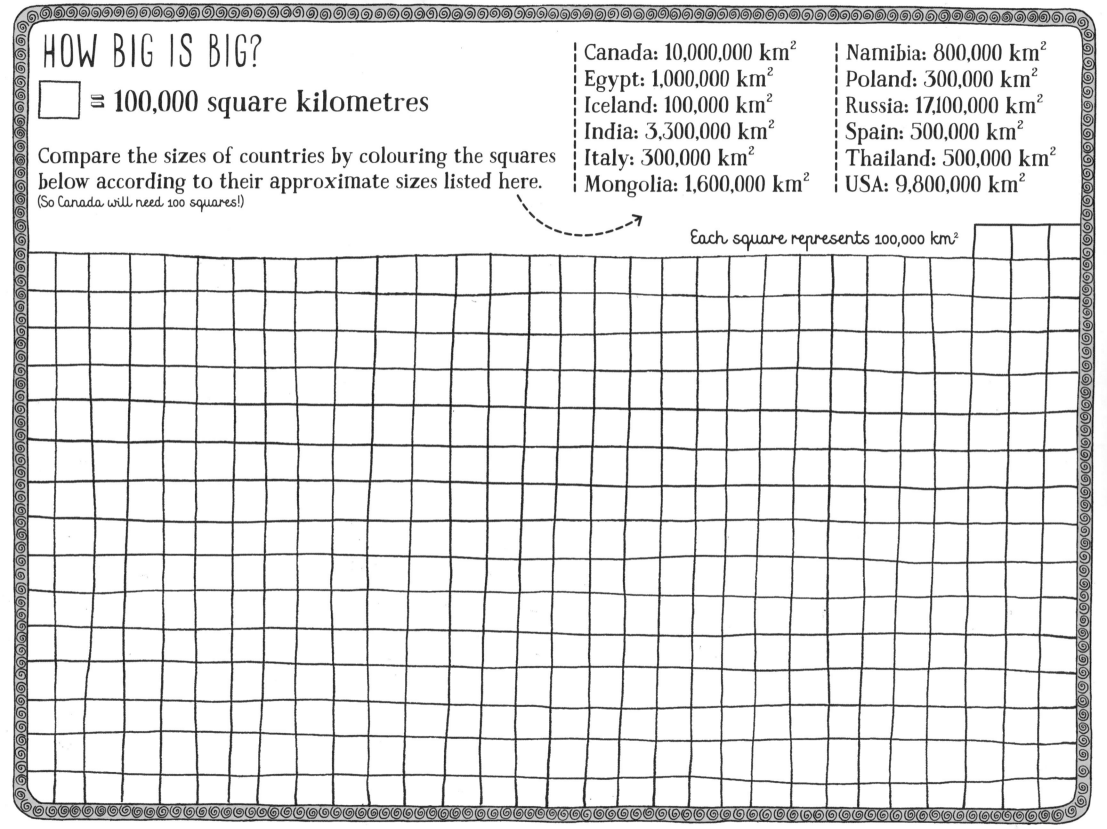

The biggest country in the world is Russia, with an area of 17,098,246 square kilometres. The smallest country is Vatican City with an area of only 0.44 square kilometres.

Imagine you are on a scuba diving holiday. Draw what you might see underwater.

COPPERBAND BUTTERFLY FISH

YELLOW TANG

BLUE DEVIL DAMSELFISH

MAHIMAHI

REEF STONEFISH

CLOWNFISH

MANDARINFISH

LEAFY SEADRAGON

Coral reefs are beautiful, but they can also be dangerous! One of the most venomous animals in the world, the blue-ringed octopus, lives in the shallow waters and coral reefs near the coast of Australia. Its body is only 5 to 10 centimetres long, but its bite could kill an adult human in minutes.

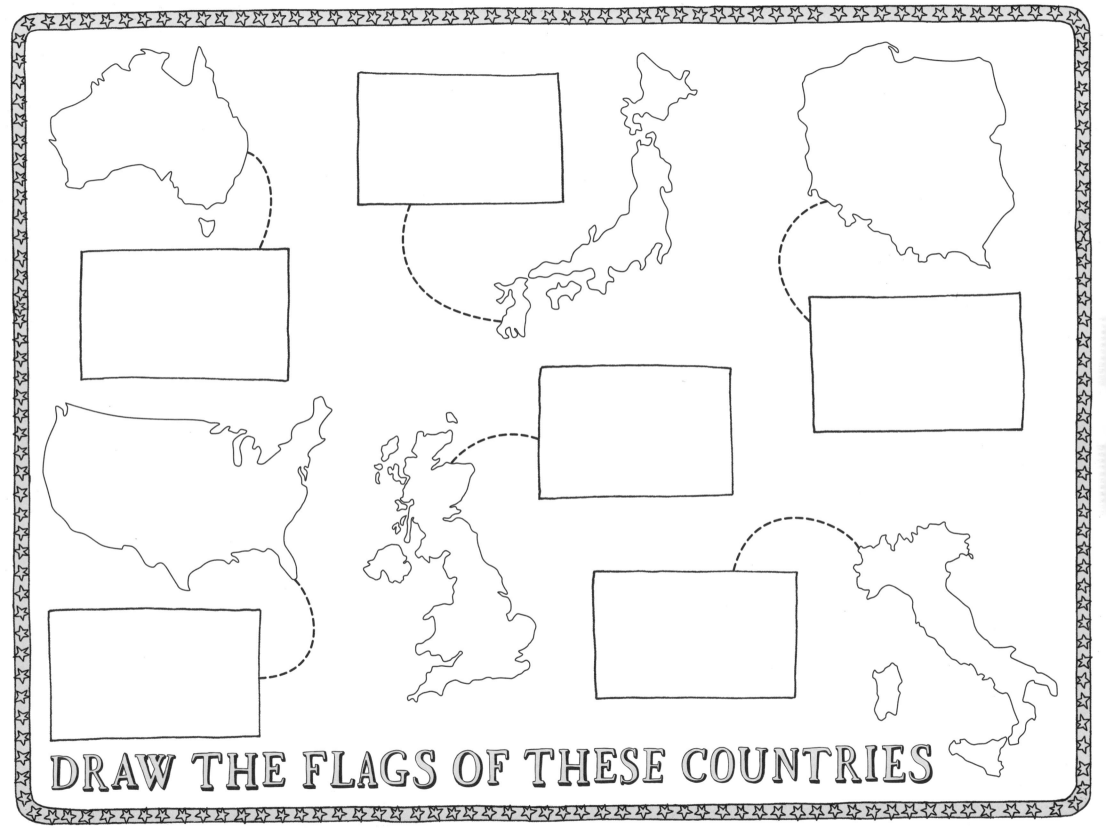

DRAW THE FLAGS OF THESE COUNTRIES

The Union Jack flies over Buckingham Palace in London when the Queen is not at home. A different flag, called the Royal Standard, flies when she is in the palace.

Draw a
global village

for different groups of friends from all corners of
the world. Add streets, shops, houses and vehicles.

On Lake Titicaca in Peru, there are entire floating villages! These are home to the Uru people, who live in small houses built on artificial islands made from reeds. Each island houses a few families.

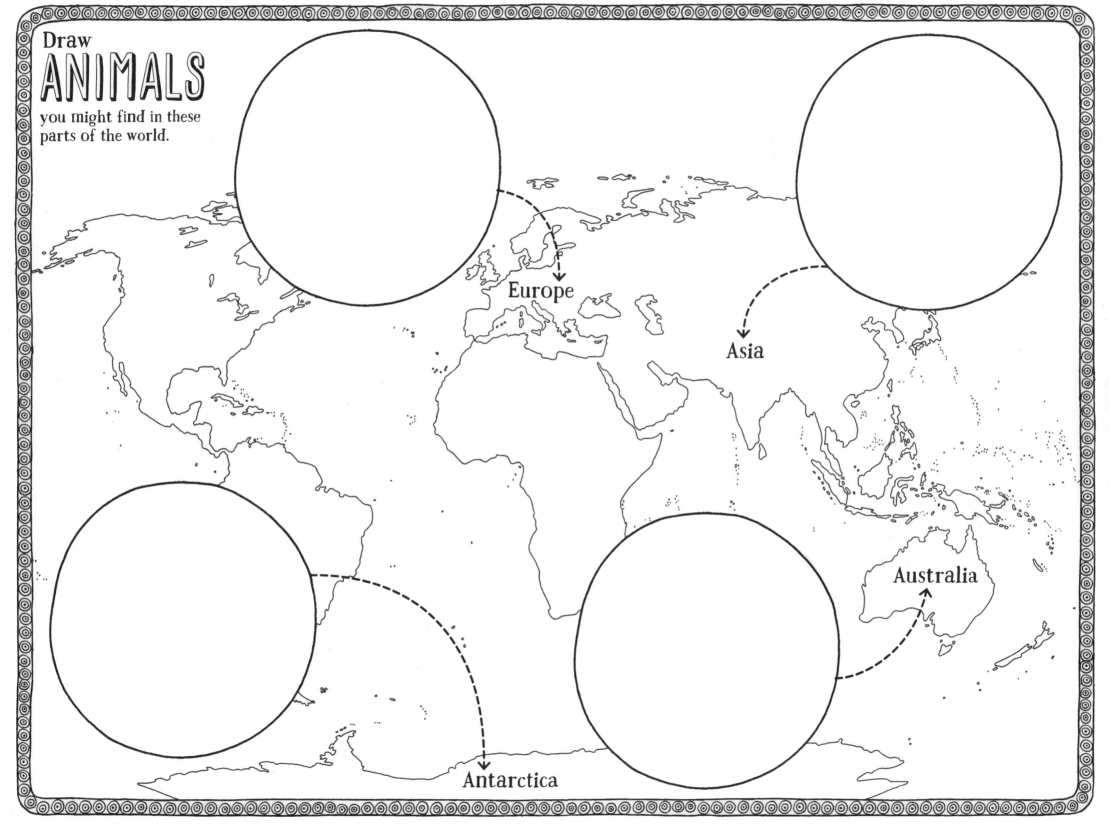

Draw
ANIMALS
you might find in these
parts of the world.

Europe

Asia

Australia

Antarctica

In the last five hundred years, many extraordinary animal species have become extinct. The giant moa bird from New Zealand is just one example, and the quagga from Africa, which looked like a zebra with stripes only on the front half of the body, is another.

Compare populations of these countries

Draw one person for each 10,000,000 inhabitants
(so France would need 6 people!).

Australia: 20,000,000
Brazil: 200,000,000
Canada: 30,000,000
Czech Republic: 10,000,000
France: 60,000,000
Japan: 130,000,000

Mexico: 110,000,000
Poland: 40,000,000
Russia: 140,000,000
South Africa: 50,000,000
United Kingdom: 60,000,000
USA: 300,000,000

In China there are 1,300,000,000 inhabitants – your stickmen wouldn't even fit on the page!

China is the country with the biggest population in the world: it is home to around 1.3 billion people. Vatican City has the smallest population, with only 840 people.

Design and colour a pattern for a KIMONO

A kimono is a traditional Japanese item of clothing.

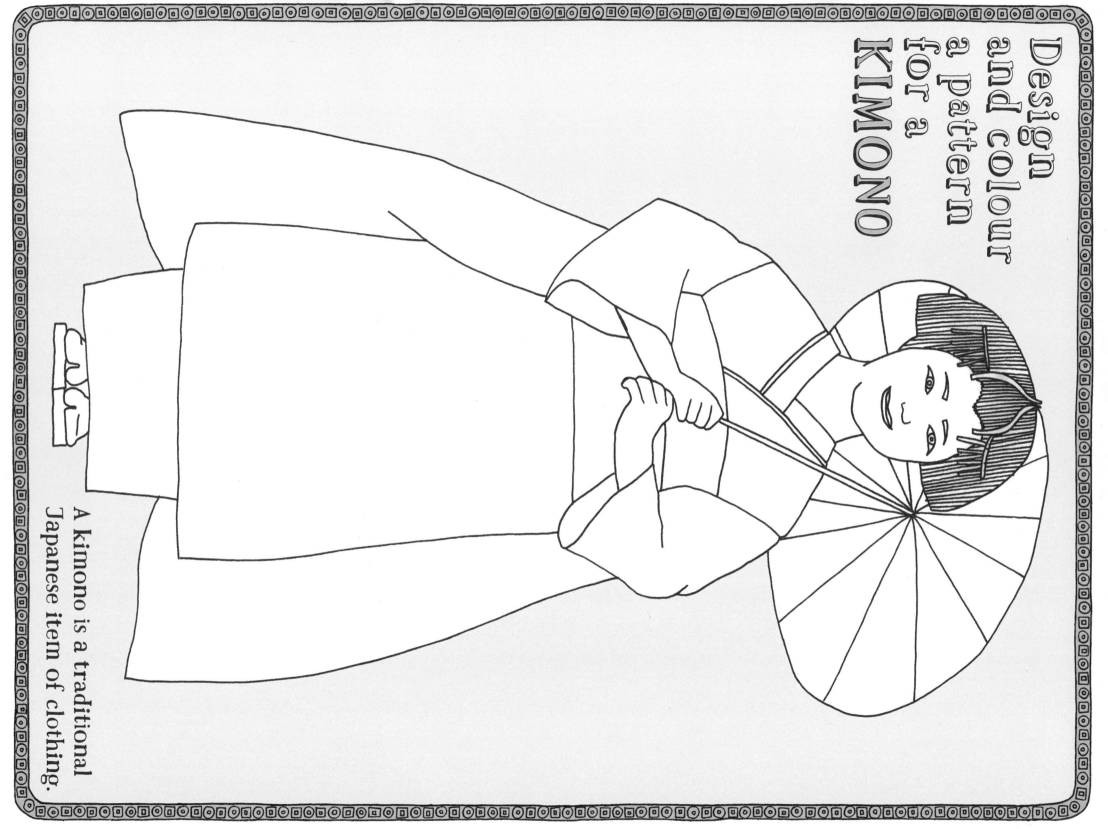

In modern Japan, kimonos are mostly worn on special occasions. A kimono consists of many pieces, which need to be matched and secured in a special way. People often hire professional assistants when putting them on to make sure they wear them properly.

Imagine that you are climbing

MOUNT EVEREST,

the highest mountain on Earth.

Draw some things you might need on the trip.

Mount Everest is known as Chomolungma in Tibet and as Sagarmatha in Nepal. Its English name is for George Everest, a British geographer who was surveyor general of India from 1830 to 1843.

IMAGINE that you are travelling across Russia on the TRANS-SIBERIAN RAILWAY. Draw what you might see during the journey.

MOSCOW

PERM

YEKATERINBURG

OMSK

NOVOSIBIRSK

KRASNOYARSK

IRKUTSK

ULAN-UDE

CHITA

KHABAROVSK

VLADIVOSTOK

It takes about six days to travel across Russia from Moscow to Vladivostok on the Trans-Siberian Railway. The train stops at a station every few hours, and the platforms of these stations are turned into small marketplaces where you can buy local food.

Draw and colour Africa's

BIG FIVE

animals on this map:

A LION, AN AFRICAN ELEPHANT, A RHINOCEROS, A CAPE BUFFALO AND A LEOPARD.

Did you know that penguins can be found in parts of Africa? Unsurprisingly, they are called African penguins. They were once numerous but are now classified an endangered species. The African penguin feeds mostly on fish and squid and makes a sound a bit like a donkey.

A castell, or human tower, is a tradition at festivals in Catalonia, Spain. People stand on one another's shoulders, sometimes ten people high! Usually a child stands at the top.

HUMAN TOWER

Finish this HUMAN TOWER with drawings of friends and family – and you!

In the Spanish town of Buñol, an extraordinary festival is held each year in August. It is called La Tomatina, and it is the world's biggest tomato fight! Imagine thousands of people throwing ripe tomatoes at each other, turning the streets red and the rivers into tomato juice! It proves that some of the world's best traditions are also the most fun.

Create a map of your NEIGHBOURHOOD

Don't forget to create a legend that explains the meaning of the colours and symbols you have used.

One of the oldest known world maps was made in the 5th century BC in Babylon, and was found in 1899 in southern Iraq. It was drawn on a clay tablet. So keep that in mind when you draw your map — some day it may be excavated by an archaeologist!